by alba

by alba

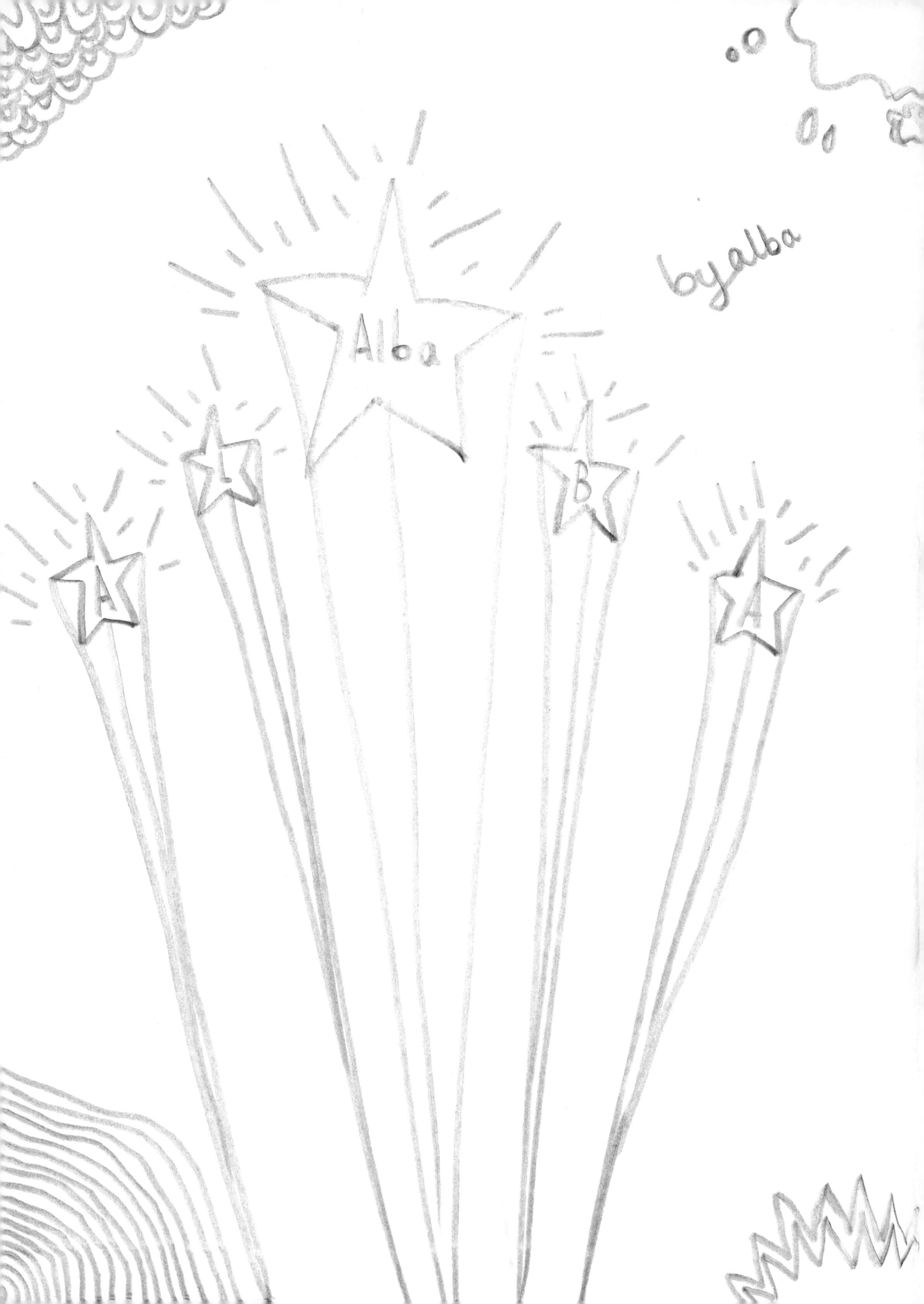
byalba
Alba
A
L
B
A

Pew!
Pew!
Pew!
Pew!
Ka-blam-erz!!!!!
Pew!
Pew!
Pew!
by alba